Hermanita
Little Sister

Written by Dr. Khalid White & Isela Garcia White, LCSW
Illustrated by Adua Hernandez

Published by Melanin Origins LLC
PO Box 122123; Arlington, TX 76012

First Edition

Library of Congress Control Number: 2019935176

ISBN: 978-1-62676-713-3 hardback

ISBN: 978-1-62676-715-7 paperback

ISBN: 978-1-62676-714-0 ebook

Dedication

This book is dedicated to all children across the land.
Continue to love. Continue to read. Continue to lead.

• • • • • • •

Dedicación

Este libro está dedicado a todos los niños de todo el país.
Continua amando. Continua leyendo. Continua liderando.

Una tarde de Sábado soleado, Ximena, Miguel y su hermanita Ariana estaban jugando Mancala.

One sunny Saturday afternoon, Ximena, Miguel, and their little sister Ariana were playing the game Mancala.

5

Podían oír a sus padres hablar
y reírse en la cocina mientras
preparaban el almuerzo para que los
niños comieran.

6

They could hear their parents talking and laughing in the kitchen as they made lunch for the kids to eat.

7

Pero Mamá y Papá no sólo estaban haciendo el almuerzo en la cocina. También estaban planeando una valiosa lección para Ximena y Miguel.

8

But mother and father were not only making lunch in that kitchen. They were also making a way for Ximena and Miguel to learn a valuable lesson.

Chores
Ximena

Miguel

Ariana

9

—Ximena, Miguel, Ariana, vengan aquí!, por favor. El almuerzo está listo.

—¡Yaaaay! —gritaron los niños mientras se apresuraron a la cocina. Su hermanita, Ariana, los siguió justo detrás de ellos.

"Ximena, Miguel, Ariana. Come in here, please. Lunch is ready!" "Yaaaay!" shouted the kids as they rushed into the kitchen to eat. Their little sister, Ariana, followed right behind them.

11

—Ximena. Miguel, tomen asiento. ¿Han oído la palabra "*responsabilidad*" antes? — preguntó su madre.

"Ximena. Miguel. Have a seat. Have you two heard of the word 'responsibility' before?" asked their mother.

—Sí. Sí, Mami—dijo Miguel.
—¡Yo también! —dijo Ximena. —Es cuando haces lo
que debes hacer. ¿No es así?

14

"Yes Mommy," said Miguel. "Me too!" said Ximena. "It's when you take care of your business. Right?"

15

—¡Así es!— dijo Mami. —¿Saben que
su hermanita los admira? Ustedes
dos pueden ayudar a guiarla de la
manera correcta. Sabemos que
pueden hacerlo.

16

"That's right. Do you know that your little sister looks up to you two? You two can help guide her in the right way," said Mommy. "We know you can do it."

17

— ¡Así es, chicos! Tu madre y yo estamos muy orgullosos de ustedes. Queremos que le enseñen a su hermanita cómo cuidar los negocios. Ustedes dos pueden enseñarle como ser responsable —dijo Papá.

18

Daddy nodded. "That's right kids. Your mother and I are very proud of you. We want you to show your little sister how to take care of business. You two can teach her responsibility.

19

—¡Está bien! —Ximena y Miguel estuvieron de acuerdo. —Podemos mostrarle a nuestra hermanita cómo lo hacemos. ¡Vamos!

"Okay," Ximena and Miguel agreed. "We can show our little sister how we do it. Let's go!"

21

Hermanita. Hermanita.
Necesitas comer tus verduras.
Hermanita. Hermanita. ¡Dios mío,
te estás poniendo pesada!

Little sister. Little sister.
You need to eat your veggies.
Little sister. Little sister.
Goodness, you're getting heavy!

23

Hermanita. Hermanita.
Te enseñaremos a jugar.
Hermanita. Hermanita.
Te enseñaremos a deletrear tu nombre.

Little sister. Little sister.
We'll show you how to play the game.
Little sister. Little sister.
We'll teach you how to spell your name.

Hermanita. Hermanita.
Está bien cometer errores.
Hermanita. Hermanita.
¡Sigue intentando y lo harás genial!

26

Little sister. Little sister.
It's okay to make mistakes.
Little sister. Little sister.
Keep trying and you'll do great!

Hermanita. Hermanita.
Nos encanta hacerte bailar.
Hermanita. Hermanita.
¡Ve a ponerte unos pantalones!

Little sister. Little sister.
We love to make you dance.
Little sister. Little sister.
Go put on some pants!

Hermanita. Hermanita.
Eres la mejor.
Hermanita. Hermanita.
¡Pero ese es el vestido de mamá!

Little sister. Little sister.
You are the very best.
Little sister. Little sister.
But that is Mommy's dress!

Hermanita. Hermanita.
Crecerás mucho, muy pronto.
Hermanita. Hermanita.
¡Inflemos el globo!

Little sister. Little sister.
You'll grow up big real soon.
Little sister. Little sister. Let's
blow up this balloon!

33

Hermanita. Hermanita.
La casa de la Abuela está en la siguiente calle.
Hermanita. Hermanita.
¡Súbete a tu asiento!

Little sister. Little sister.
Grandma's house is down the street.
Little sister. Little sister.
Get in your car seat!

Hermanita. Hermanita.
Ayudemos a Papi a hacer espagueti.
Hermanita. Hermanita.
Le fascina a Mamá, "¡La cena está lista!".

Little sister. Little sister.
Let's help Daddy make spaghetti.
Little sister. Little sister.
We'll tell Mommy, "Dinner's ready!"

Hermanita. Hermanita.
Todos podemos compartir
nuestros juguetes.
Hermanita. Hermanita.
Te ayudaremos a lavarte el pelo.

Little sister. Little sister.
All our toys we can share.
Little sister. Little sister.
We'll help you wash your hair

Hermanita. Hermanita.
Es hora de ir a la cama.
Hermanita. Hermanita.
Has oído lo que acabamos de decir?

40

Little sister. Little sister.
Now it's time to go to bed.
Little sister. Little sister.
Did you hear what we just said?

41

Hermanita. Hermanita.
¡Tuvimos un buen día!
Hermanita. Hermanita.
Te mostraremos cómo rezar.

42

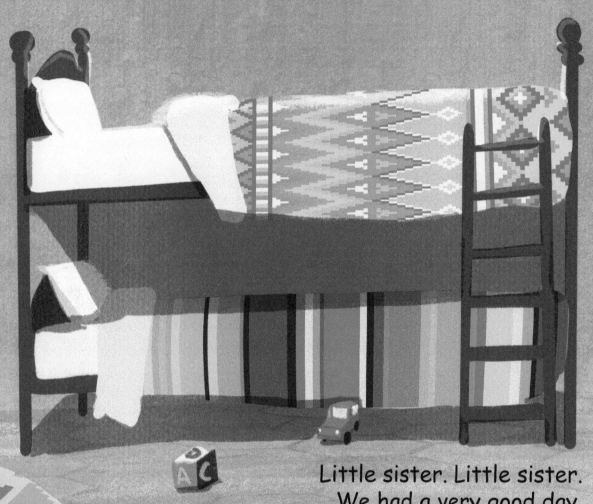

Little sister. Little sister.
We had a very good day.
Little sister. Little sister.
We'll show you how to pray.

43

What do you want to be when you grow up?
Please write or draw your ideas.

¿Qué quieres ser cuando seas grande?
Por favor escribe o dibuja tus ideas.

What things do you like to do with your family?
Please write or draw your ideas.

¿Qué cosas te gusta hacer con tu familia?
Por favor escribe o dibuja tus ideas.

46

What are ways that you will help your family in the future?
Please write or draw your ideas.

¿En qué forma ayudarás a tu familia en el futuro?
Por favor escribe o dibuja tus ideas.

About the Author:

Dr. Khalid Akil White is an award-winning educator, author and filmmaker.
Khalid has worked with youth and young adults, in public education, for 15 years.
As an entrepreneur, Khalid owns and operates Blkmpwr (Black Empower), LLC.,
a multi-media company charged with creating counter-narrative content.
Visit his website for details:
www.blkmpwr.com

Sobre el Autor:

Dr. Khalid Akil White es un educador, autor y cinematografo galardonado.
Khalid ha trabajado con jóvenes y adultos, en educación pública, durante 15 años.
Como empresario, Khalid posee y opera Blkmpwr (Black Empower), LLC.,
una empresa multimedia a cargo de crear contenido contra-narrativo.
Visite su website para más detalles:
www.blkmpwr.com

@BLKMPWR

About the Author:

Isela Garcia White is a Licensed Clinical Social Worker dedicated to providing high quality, effective and culturally responsive mental health services to children and families from diverse communities.

She earned her BA from UC Berkeley and her MSW from the University of Southern California.

Sobre el Autor:

Isela Garcia White es una Licenciada Trabajadora Social dedicada a brindar servicios de salud mental de alta calidad, efectivos y culturalmente receptivos a niños y familias de diversas comunidades.

Obtuvo su BA de UC Berkeley y su MSW de la University of Southern California.

A big Thank You to Mrs. Maria Garcia for her translation assistance.

Un gran agradecimiento a la Sra. María García por su asistencia en la traducción.